SNAIL HITS THE TRAIL

Written by
Laura Appleton-Smith

Illustrated by
Preston Neel

Laura Appleton-Smith was born and raised in Vermont and holds a degree in English from Middlebury College. Laura is a primary school teacher who has combined her talents in creative writing and her experience in early childhood education to create *Books to Remember*. Laura lives in New Hampshire with her husband, Terry.

Preston Neel was born in Macon, Georgia. Greatly inspired by Dr. Seuss, he decided to become an artist at the age of four. Preston's advanced art studies took place at the Academy of Art College San Francisco. Now Preston pursues his career in art with the hope of being an inspiration himself, particularly to children who want to explore their endless bounds.

A Book to Remember™
Published by Flyleaf Publishing

For orders or information, contact us at **(800) 449-7006**.
Please visit our website at **www.flyleafpublishing.com**

Eighth Edition 2/20
Library of Congress Catalog Card Number: 2002090762
ISBN-13: 978-1-929262-12-0
Printed and bound in the USA at Worzalla Publishing, Stevens Point, WI

For Preston, for being you...
You have added so much to my stories over the years.
The visual worlds you create are magical.
Thank you, as always, for sharing your talents.

LAS

For me, with special thanks to Stormy the Parrot.

PN

CHAPTER ONE

Once upon a time, on the banks of an African bay, there lived one hundred snails.

The snails spent their days wending their way from the land to the bay and back again.

The snails were content to slug from sunup to sunset day after day.
All of the snails, that is, but Ray. Ray complained and complained…

3

"If I had legs I would hit the trail. If I had wings I would sail into the air. I would visit distant lands if I were not stuck as a snail."

The rest of the snails felt that Ray's complaints were in vain.
"Once a snail always a snail," they would say.
But they did suspect that Ray was different in a way...

5

Ray had a trait no snail could explain.
The trails left by the rest of the snails' tails were a dull gray,
but the trail left by Ray's tail was a rainbow.

6

Chapter Two

One day Ray was training to slug and slip faster.
"No pain no gain," he huffed as he strained,
but Ray was not a bit faster.

Ray could not contain himself.
He flopped onto the sand and flailed and wailed in dismay.

8

Just then, an African Gray Parrot landed next to him. "Tell me your pains," he said.

"I am a slug of a snail," Ray sniffled and snuffled. "I will never be fast and get away. I will end up stuck on the banks of this bay for the rest of my days."

10

"My granddad Parrot has a saying. 'If there is a will, there is a way,' he says.

If you dwell on the fact that you are stuck then you will remain stuck.
But you can train your brain to invent different ways to travel.
If you do not have legs, get legs; get wings; get into and onto things."

11

"I get it!" said Ray.
It was as if a ray of sun had lit on his brain.

From then on, Ray went about things in a different way.

CHAPTER THREE

The next day, Ray slugged his way to the bay
with the rest of the snails.

He crept up next to a man who was explaining
that he was getting on a train.

Ray did not delay. He snuck into the man's backpack.
He tucked himself in next to the man's cameras and waited.

TRAIN 9

TRAVEL AFRICA

"Clack, clack, clack," went the train on its tracks.
  When the man was tucked in his bed Ray crept from the backpack.

The wind swept past. Ray had never traveled so fast!
  As the train sped over the land Ray could not contain himself.

Out of happiness, he wept.

The next day Ray hid himself on the brim of the man's hat.
What a vista Ray had from where he sat!

There was a big rainbow blimp waiting to sail up into the air.
The man's camera lens went "snap, snap, snap."

When the man went up to the blimp and stepped in,
Ray just about fell from the hat's brim.
"This must be my lucky day!" Ray exclaimed.

Up into the air the blimp lifted.
The man snapped his camera at the animals
on the grasslands as they drifted.

Ray felt he had been gifted.
He did not understand that so many animals existed.

The blimp was drifting over hills of volcanic rock by midday.
The volcanic lava was hot and red and it bubbled and sprayed.

What a display!
Ray could not wait to tell the snails back at the bay.

When the blimp landed a cab was waiting to pick up the man. But it was not long until the cab got stuck in a traffic jam.

"I am going to miss my next trip," the man complained. The cab driver honked and yelled, but in vain.

Ray was glad, in a way, that snails did not travel fast and get into traffic jams.

At last, the cab stopped next to a boat named the *Hail Gail*.

The man paid the cab driver and jumped onto the boat just as it sailed away.

CHAPTER FOUR

Ray was glad to rest in the man's cabin
when he left his hat and went to dinner.

The sailboat bobbed on the swells as the sun set.
As the wind picked up, Ray began to fret.

Ray felt afraid. Would he get back to his bay again?

"If there is a will, there is a way," Ray thought he heard the Parrot say.
Ray drifted off for a nap as the sailboat began to sway.

28

Suddenly, Ray was up.

The sailboat was swaying and it was raining.

It was not long until the sailboat was rocking and it was hailing.

The wind gusted and the sail ripped from the mast.

Ray had to get away fast.

The man ran into the cabin and grabbed his camera bag and his hat (and Ray), and ran onto the deck into the wind and the hail and the spray.

The sailors yelled, "Bail! Bail!" as they bailed with their pails.

Just then, the wind gusted a big gust that lifted the man's hat up over the rails.

The hat landed in the bay.
Ray held on to the brim as the hat tossed and rocked and swayed.

Ray felt that this must be it—this was his end.
He would never be back at his bay again.

He held on to the brim of the hat and waited...
Ray was afraid. In dismay, he fainted.

CHAPTER FIVE

"It is Ray, it is Ray," Ray heard his snails say.
The sun was up and Ray was back on the banks of his bay.

Had his trip just been a dream?

Then Ray spotted the man's hat.
He had a fantastic trip and he was back…

Ray slugged the rest of his days
with the rest of the snails without complaint.

As he slugged he left his rainbow trail
and filled the rest of the snails' brains
with tales of his trips to lands far away.

And when snails asked him if they could fulfill their dreams,
Ray could tell them, "If there is a will, there is a way."

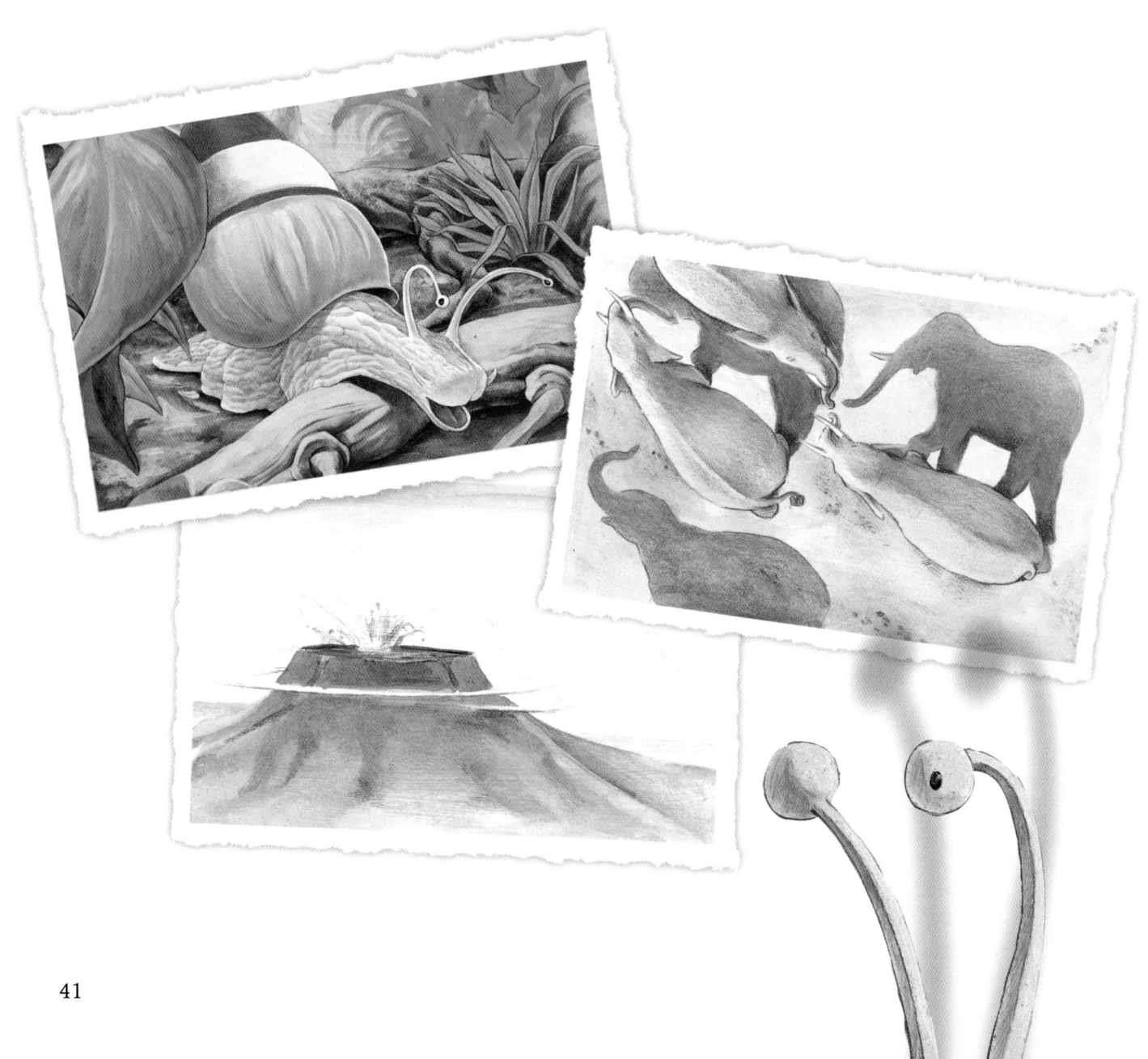

41

Prerequisite Skills

Single consonants and short vowels
Final double consonants **ff**, **gg**, **ll**, **nn**, **ss**, **tt**, **zz**
Consonant /k/ **ck**
Consonant /j/ **g**, **dge**
Consonant /s/ **c**
/ng/ **n[k]**
Consonant digraphs /ng/ **ng**, /th/ **th**, /hw/ **wh**
Consonant digraphs /ch/ **ch**, **tch**, /sh/ **sh**, /f/ **ph**
Schwa /ə/ **a, e, i, o, u**
Long /ā/ **a_e**
Long /ē/ **e_e, ee, y**
Long /ī/ **i_e, igh**
Long /ō/ **o_e**
Long /ū/, /o͞o/ **u_e**
r-Controlled /ar/ **ar**
r-Controlled /or/ **or**
r-Controlled /ûr/ **er, ir, ur, ear, or, [w]or**
/ô/ **al, all**
/ul/ **le**
/d/ or /t/ **–ed**

Target Letter-Sound Correspondence	
Long /ā/ sound spelled **ai**	
afraid	rails
bail	raining
bailed	sail
brain	sailed
brains	sailors
complained	snail
complaint	snail's
complaints	snails
contain	snails'
exclaimed	strained
explain	tail
explaining	tails
fainted	trail
flailed	trails
Gail	train
gain	training
hail	trait
hailing	vain
paid	wailed
pails	wait
pain	waited
pains	waiting

Target Letter-Sound Correspondence	
Long /ā/ sound spelled **ay**	
always	Ray's
away	say
bay	saying
day	spray
days	sprayed
dismay	sway
display	swayed
gray	swaying
midday	way
Ray	ways

Story Puzzle Words

boat	happiness
delay	onto
dream	rainbow
dreams	remain
fulfill	sailboat

High-Frequency Puzzle Words

about	from	once	to
again	going	one	two
air	have	out	was
are	he	over	were
be	into	said	what
been	lived	says	where
began	many	so	who
by	me	their	without
could	my	there	would
do	no	they	you
four	of	thought	your

44

Decodable Words

a	crept	granddad	just	rest	the
African	deck	grasslands	land	ripped	them
after	did	gust	landed	rock	then
all	different	gusted	lands	rocked	things
am	dinner	had	last	rocking	this
an	distant	has	lava	sand	three
and	drifted	hat	left	sat	time
animals	drifting	hat's	legs	set	tossed
as	driver	heard	lens	slip	tracks
asked	dull	held	lifted	slug	traffic
at	dwell	hid	lit	slugged	travel
back	end	hills	long	snap	traveled
backpack	existed	him	lucky	snapped	trip
bag	fact	himself	man	sniffled	trips
banks	fantastic	his	man's	snuck	tucked
bed	far	hit	mast	snuffled	understand
big	fast	hits	miss	sped	until
bit	faster	honked	must	spent	up
blimp	fell	hot	named	spotted	upon
bobbed	felt	huffed	nap	stepped	visit
brim	filled	hundred	never	stopped	vista
bubbled	five	I	next	stuck	volcanic
but	flopped	if	not	suddenly	wending
cab	for	in	off	sun	went
cabin	fret	invent	on	sunset	wept
camera	get	is	parrot	suspect	when
cameras	getting	it	past	swells	will
can	gifted	its	pick	swept	wind
chapter	glad	jam	picked	tales	wings
clack	got	jams	ran	tell	with
content	grabbed	jumped	red	that	yelled